MARINE FISH

MARINE FISH

THE RECOGNITION AND TREATMENT OF DISEASES

DIAGNOSTIC SERIES NO. 1

ROBERT R. CLIFTON

Printed in the United States of America

LIBRARY OF CONGRESS NUMBER - 87-090469
FIRST EDITION
ISBN 0-9618625-5-6

Acknowledgements

I would like to gratefully acknowledge and thank the many individuals who made this manual possible through their knowledge and skills, and their willingness to give freely of both.

For the illustrations I would like to thank Mario Rojas who, with a talent enviable by anyone, drew all the artwork contained herein. The cover was designed by Jonathan Ingram. The idea for the diagnostic chart was taken from the book by Dr. Edward Kingsford, *Treatment of Exotic Marine Fish Diseases*. There are many individuals who helped by reviewing the text material; to these people I also give my sincere thanks.

Preface

For many years there has been a tremendous lack of ability to recognize the varied types of diseases and parasites that afflict marine fish. While there are individuals who are knowledgeable in this field, their research and findings are not readily available to the marine hobbyist. There will always be times of complete confusion and disgust, but these should be tempered with knowledge and the desire to learn more about what might be causing the problem or problems.

There are diseases that are not discussed in this book because of their rarity of occurrence. I have chosen to concentrate on the diseases and parasites that the home aquarist will most often encounter in a salt-water tank. There is also great confusion as to the treatment to be used once the problem has been properly diagnosed. This is certainly understandable considering the amount of time involved in isolating an organism and then finding an effective treatment.

It is the purpose of this text not only to bring together information from numerous and varied texts, but also to compliment and simplify this information for the marine aquarist. Any marine aquarist needs to arm himself with as much information as possible concerning treatment of diseases and parasites; hopefully this book will allow anyone from novice to expert to diagnose and treat virtually all diseases that afflict marine fish in the home aquarium.

To my parents, without whose help and support this would have been a difficult task.

Contents

1

Quarantine Procedure

It must always be assumed that all fish are suffering, or are carriers of a disease or parasite. It is therefore risky to introduce any new fish directly to an established and healthy tank. The use of a hospital or quarantine tank is highly recommended, although this is not always feasible or possible.

If you are interested in a fish that is a new arrival, ask the store to hold it for four to six days. Most stores will be happy to accommodate your request. However, if they will not, and you are unfamiliar with the store, you might consider taking your business elsewhere. The professional fish store owner should know how to detect and treat infected fish and should have the facilities to do so. If the fish is a carrier of an infection, the store should have had time to detect it and treat it before you contaminate your tank. If you buy a fish that has not been observed for several days, it should always be quarantined. It is also better to deal with a limited number of stores, so that if you do have a problem with a fish you can go back to the store and see if they are having the same problem in their tanks.

If a hospital tank is utilized, the water should be maintained at the same temperature, pH, and salinity as the tank in which the fish are to be introduced. At this point there is some difference of opinion as to whether the quarantine tank should be treated with various medica-

tions or used as an observation tank unless a disease is noticed. The choice is yours, but many diseases are very difficult to treat once the symptoms appear. The following medications can be added to the tank as a precaution or, depending on the problem, specific treatments can be introduced as needed.
Methylene blue: ..2 drops per gallon. Repeated every other day or when the blue coloration has completely disappeared. Repeat for 3 treatments.
Kanamycin: ..200 mg. per 10 gal. This should be repeated every other day for five days.
Copper sulfate : ...15 ppm. This can be monitored with a test kit to maintain the proper level.
Isoniazid: .. 40 mg. per gal. This should be repeated every other day for 3 treatments.

NOTE: TURN ALL CARBON FILTRATION OFF DURING TREATMENT BECAUSE ACTIVATED CHARCOAL WILL REMOVE THE MEDICATION.

The hospital tank should be monitored closely for any increase in ammonia and nitrites. A 25% water change should be made every other day and the treatment level of the medications brought back up to the proper level.
Methelyne Blue can be obtained from any pet store. Kanamycin is available in many antibiotic remedies on the market and can be bought in almost any pet store under different names. Kanamycin can also be obtained through your local veterinarian. Copper Sulfate is available under many different trade names also and is readily available in a pet store. Isoniazid is available only through a veterinarian. Remedies that contain some Isoniazid are available through pet stores, but are not recommended.
The ammonia and nitrite levels must be monitored closely in a hospital tank because of the lack of a biological filter. The ammonia can be maintained at a low level through the use of ammonia removing chips or liquid remover as well as by water changes which will also lower the nitrite level. Water changes are the only effective way

to maintain acceptable nitrite levels.* Nitrex is a commercially available product that will remove nitrite, but it also removes any medications.

If a hospital tank is not utilized and you wish to introduce the fish to the main tank, the tank can be treated with copper sulfate in the same manner as you would a hospital tank. However, copper sulfate is lethal to all invertebrates except hermit crabs, who seem to do fine at the recommended treatment level. Be very careful about adding antibiotics to the main tank because of the possible damage that could occur to the biologcal filter.

*Nitrites would not be present in a tank lacking a biological filter.

2

Disease Diagnostic Chart for Marine Fish

Introduction:

The following chart has been designed to aid in identification of the symptoms and appropriate diagnosis of fish disease*

Adapted with permission from The Treatment of Exotic Marine Fish Diseases *by* *Edward Kingsford, copyright 1975, Palmetto Press.*

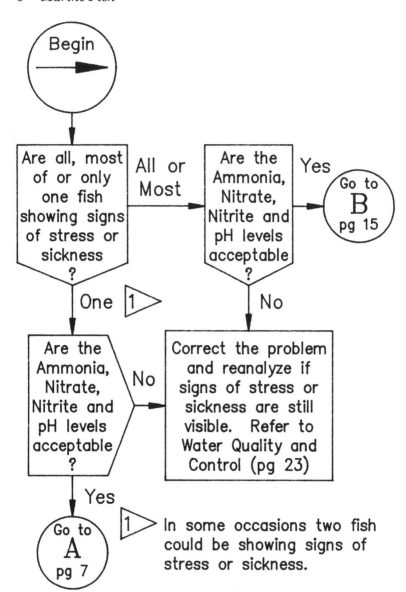

Begin

Are all, most of or only one fish showing signs of stress or sickness ?

All or Most

Are the Ammonia, Nitrate, Nitrite and pH levels acceptable ?

Yes — Go to B pg 15

One 1

No

Are the Ammonia, Nitrate, Nitrite and pH levels acceptable ?

No

Correct the problem and reanalyze if signs of stress or sickness are still visible. Refer to Water Quality and Control (pg 23)

Yes

Go to A pg 7

1 ▷ In some occasions two fish could be showing signs of stress or sickness.

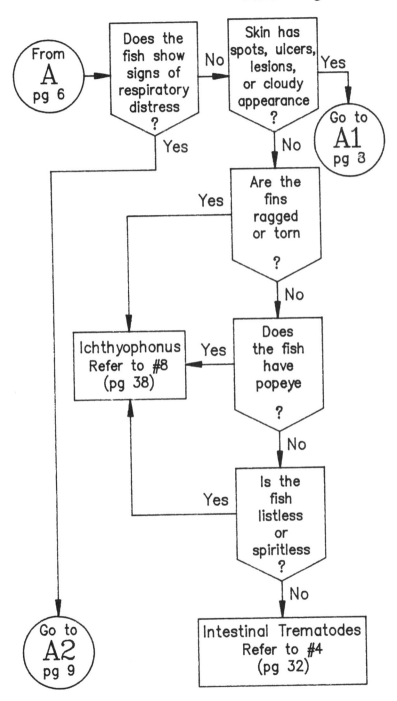

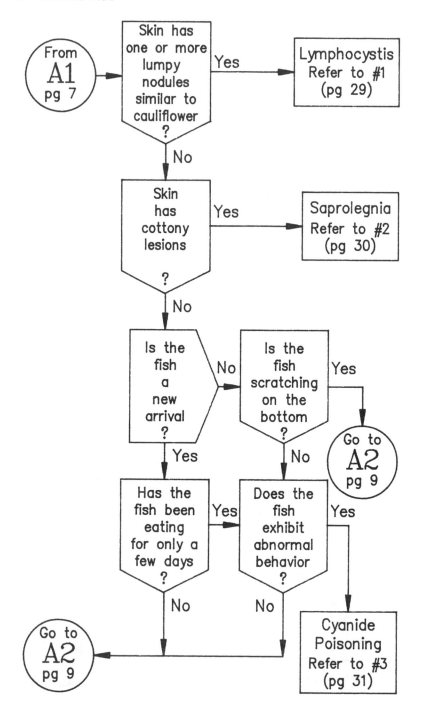

From
A1
pg 7

Skin has one or more lumpy nodules similar to cauliflower ?

Yes → Lymphocystis Refer to #1 (pg 29)

No ↓

Skin has cottony lesions ?

Yes → Saprolegnia Refer to #2 (pg 30)

No ↓

Is the fish a new arrival ?

No → Is the fish scratching on the bottom ?

Yes → Go to **A2** pg 9

Yes ↓ (Is the fish a new arrival)

No ↓ (Is the fish scratching on the bottom)

Has the fish been eating for only a few days ?

Yes → Does the fish exhibit abnormal behavior ?

Yes → Cyanide Poisoning Refer to #3 (pg 31)

No ↓ (Has the fish been eating)

No ↓ (Does the fish exhibit abnormal behavior)

Go to **A2** pg 9

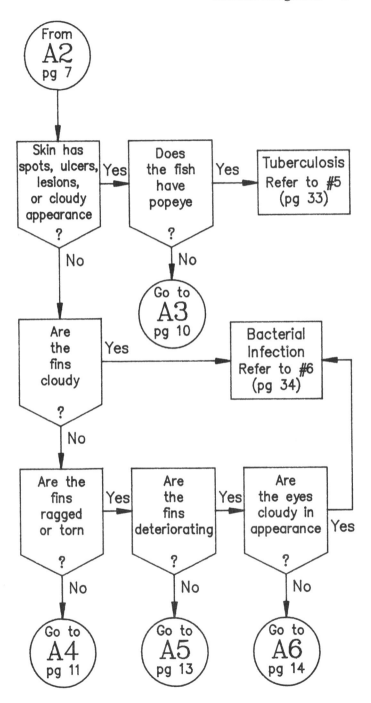

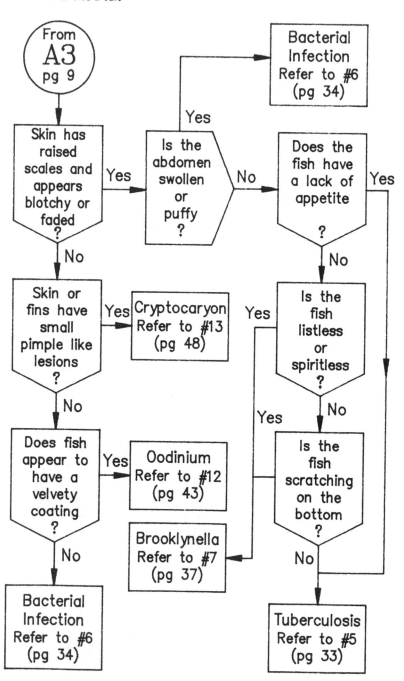

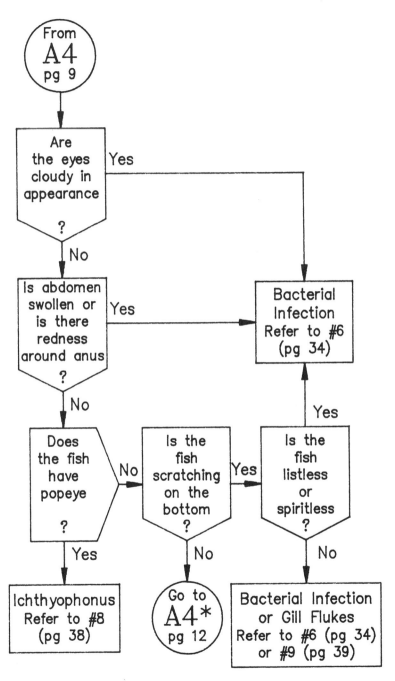

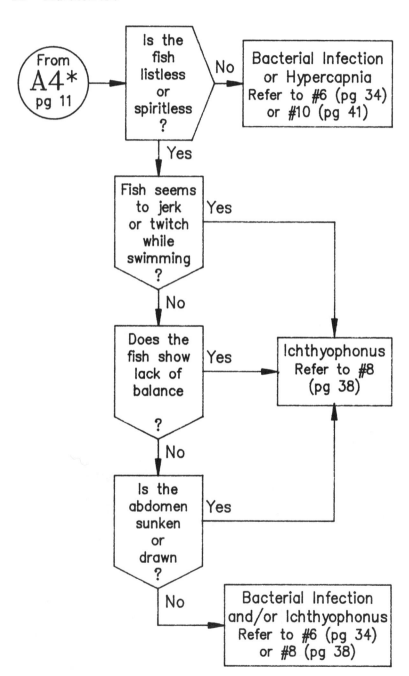

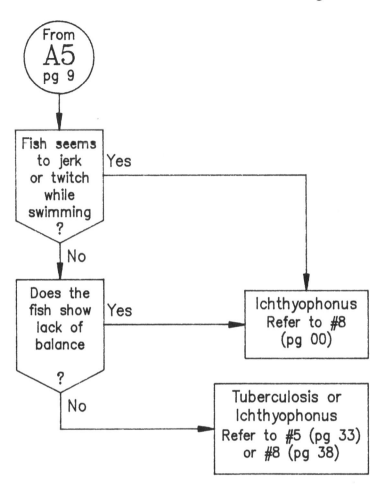

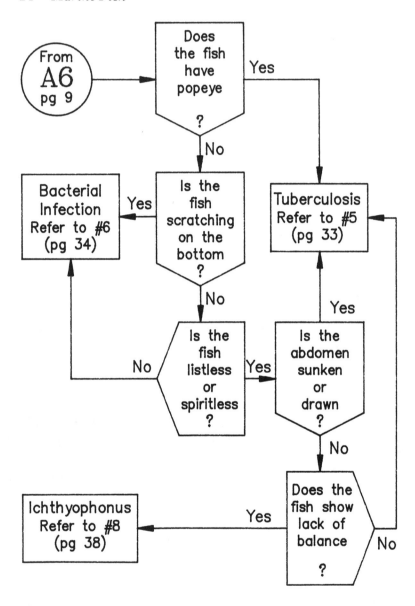

From
A6
pg 9

Does the fish have popeye ?

Yes

No

Bacterial Infection Refer to #6 (pg 34)

Yes

Is the fish scratching on the bottom ?

No

Tuberculosis Refer to #5 (pg 33)

Yes

No

Is the fish listless or spiritless ?

Yes

Is the abdomen sunken or drawn ?

No

Ichthyophonus Refer to #8 (pg 38)

Yes

Does the fish show lack of balance ?

No

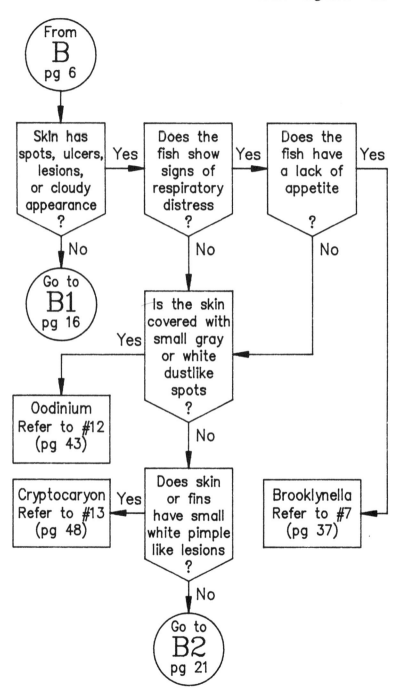

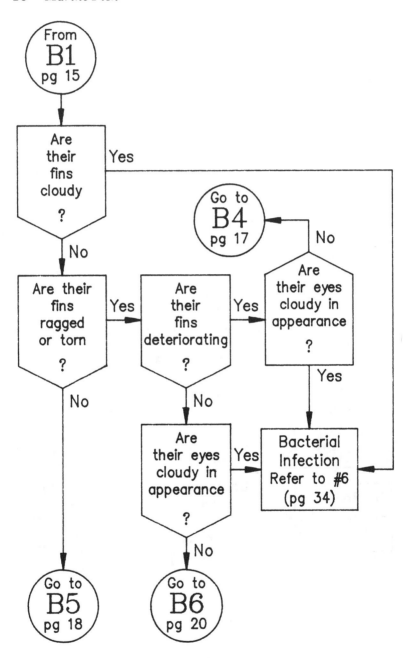

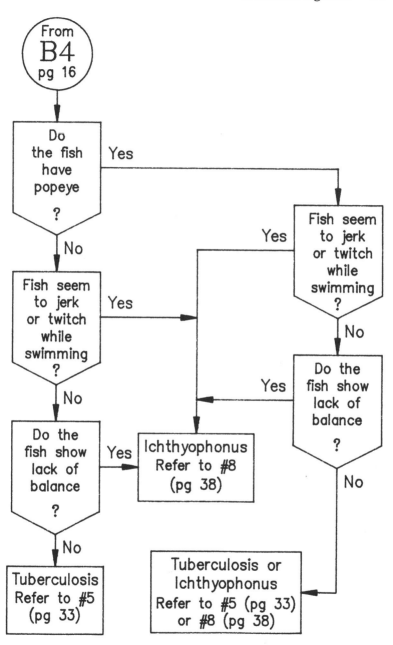

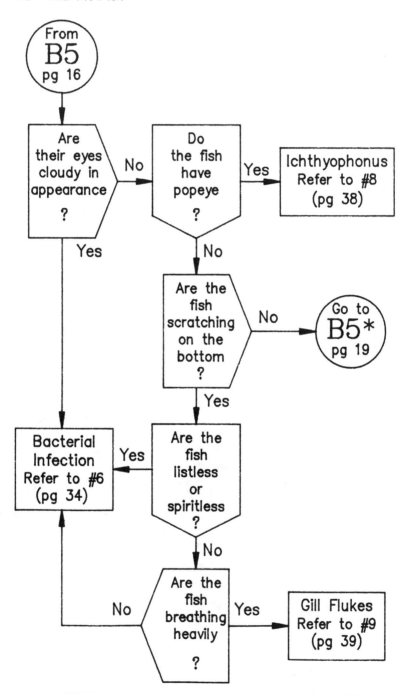

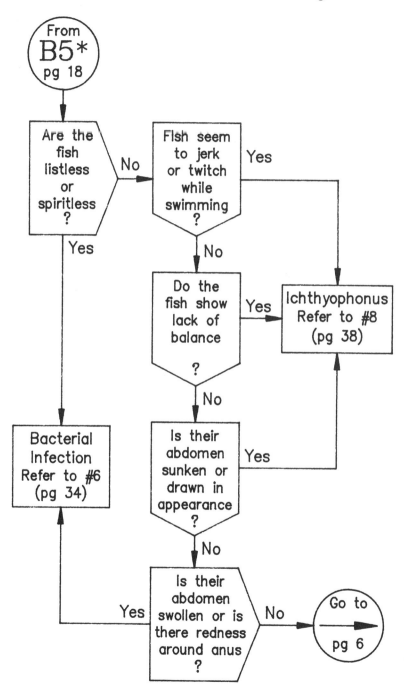

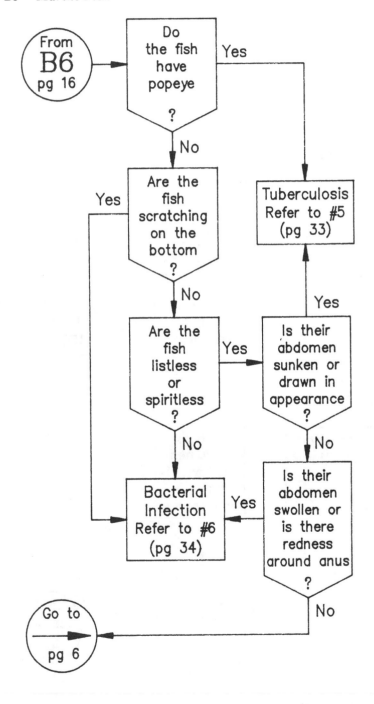

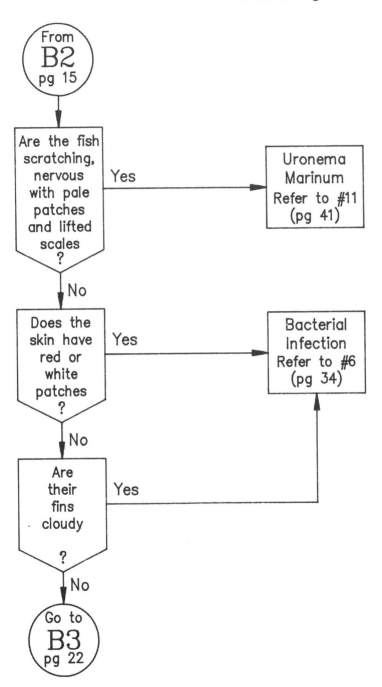

From
B2
pg 15

Are the fish scratching, nervous with pale patches and lifted scales ?

Yes

Uronema Marinum Refer to #11 (pg 41)

No

Does the skin have red or white patches ?

Yes

Bacterial Infection Refer to #6 (pg 34)

No

Are their fins cloudy ?

Yes

No

Go to
B3
pg 22

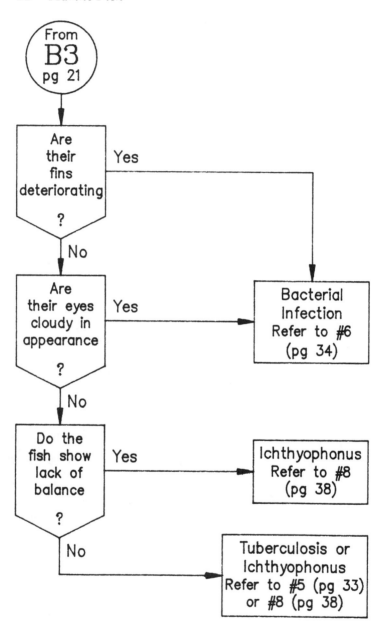

3

Water Quality and Control

The following pages contain brief outlines of salt-water quality limits and the control of these limits under aquarium conditions. There are always exceptions to any rule, and the specifications of different chemical characteristics such as pH, salinity, and nitrogenous waste build-up will vary with different types of fish. The aquarist should learn as much as possible about each fish in the aquarium in order to secure the environmental requirements for each species.

Temperature

Thermal stress is one of the greatest stress factors placed on fish and should be avoided at all costs. The body temperature of an ectothermic animal is controlled by the temperature of the environment in which it is placed, in this case the water. Therefore, the temperature of the water in which it is to be placed should be as close as possible to that of the water from which it came. Floating the fish in the tank prior to introducing them to the water allows their body temperatures to adjust to the new environment. Fish should never be introduced to a new tank without first acclimatizing them to the water temperature.

The range of temperatures for marine fish will vary according to the depth that the fish naturally inhabits and the ocean in which it is found. However, for the purpose of this book, we will consider only the tropical species that are common in depths of less than 100 feet. For these fish the range of temperatures will fall between 75 and 80 degrees fahrenheit. In order to maintain the aquarium at the proper temperature, you should be aware of the proper wattage of heater that is needed for that particular aquarium size. The following formula will help in determining the size heater that is needed:

$$\Delta T \, ((A1 \times .63 \times 10^{-4}) + (A2 \times .65 \times 10^{-4})) \times 48.76 = \text{Continuous}$$
Wattage needed

ΔT = Difference in the temperature in the room and the desired temperature of the aquarium
A1 = Surface area of the glass in cm^2
A2 = Surface area of the water in cm^2

A steady temperature should always be maintained in the room where the aquarium is located, as this will greatly help prevent additional difficulties maintaining a stable temperature in the aquarium. This book will not deal with cooling units as this involves a great deal of expense and is not a concern for the average aquarist.

pH

The term pH denotes the concentration of hydrogen ions or hydroxyl ions in a given solution. The concentration of these ions determines the alkalinity or acidity of the solution. pH is affected by so many different chemical changes and various other factors that this book is not going to describe and detail each one. The pH of natural seawater is 8.2. A pH of 8.0 to 8.5 is acceptable as long as it does not fluctuate up and down. A pH as low as 7.8 is not acceptable because fish are not accustomed to this low pH level.

There are several products on the market that are designed to buffer the pH, and they do seem to work rather well. However, the need to use any of these products raises a question of whether the aquarium is being maintained properly. In a closed system it is difficult to simulate the ocean's biosystem. Therefore, the water is going to need some form of regeneration either through chemical additives, or through the practice of regular water changes, or both.

Ammonia

Ammonia is the most toxic naturally occurring chemical compound in the marine aquarium. Ammonia is more toxic in the marine aquarium because of the higher pH values of the water. There is ten times more unionised ammonia at a pH of 8.0 than there is at a pH of 7.0. Details regarding the toxicity of ammonia would require an entire chapter and will therefore not be explored further. The interest here is in maintaining the ammonia at a level of 0.00 ppm.

In a newly set up aquarium the ammonia is the first thing to rise due to fish excrement and other metabolic wastes. A type of bacteria called *Nitrosommonas* grows in the tank and uses the ammonia for food. The *Nitrosommonas* keep the ammonia at acceptable levels and also produce a waste product called *nitrite*. The nitrite is consumed by another bacteria called *Nitrobacters;* these bacteria produce a waste that is called *nitrate*. Nitrates are the least poisonous of the nitrogen cycle and therefore of the least concern. The ammonia is always kept at an acceptable level until the tank is overloaded, overfed, or the biological filter is disturbed. The use of a gram negative antibiotic could result in the destruction of the filter bed.

There are many products on the market to remove ammonia, but these should not be used unless the ammonia is at such a level as to cause a stressful situation on the fish. The reason for not using an ammonia removing product is because it slows the development of a good bacterial filter bed. It is a good idea to keep such a product on hand in case of an emergency.

Nitrite

Nitrite is the second most poisonous naturally occurring chemical in the aquarium and is the by-product of *Nitrosomonas* bacteria feeding on ammonia. Nitrite is toxic because it is capable of oxidizing hemoglobin, thereby producing methemoglobin, which is incapable of transporting oxygen. Methemoglobin can be recognized in the gills as a brown discoloration. It has been suggested that methemoglobin can be produced by transporting fish in bags pressurized with pure oxygen.

Nitrite is usually not a serious problem unless left at high concentrations or unless the fish are exposed for extended periods of time. If the fish do become stressed because of a high nitrite level, the best remedy is a partial water change to help alleviate the stress on the fish. It is also necessary to determine what disturbed the filterbed or why the nitrite level has risen.

Nitrate

A second type of bacteria grows in the tank and feeds on the nitrites; these bacteria are called *Nitrobacters* and their waste is called *nitrate*.

Nitrate is not generally a problem with teleosts, although there are some fish which cannot thrive in an aquarium if the nitrate level is allowed to reach high levels. The author has had tanks with levels as high as 1200 ppm and experienced no problems with teleosts, however these levels were reduced in less than 48 hours. The average nitrate level that has been found acceptable is 60 ppm and below. The nitrate should be controlled with regular water changes and a good algae growth, which should be harvested regularly. On wet dry filtration systems that utilize a denitra filter, nitrates are not a problem if the filter is maintained properly.

Salinity

The specific gravity of water will vary from tank to tank in some degree. Most fish will thrive in a salinity of 1.018 to 1.025. The exceptions are the fish from the Red Sea, which like to stay around the upper end of this range at about 1.024. Corals are another exception to the salinity range in that they also prefer a high specific gravity. With all other fish, 1.019 to 1.021 is the most acceptable range for two reasons: (a) It slows the fish's metabolism; and (b) it allows for evaporation so that the salinity does not get too high before the water is replaced.

It should be noted that when nitrate is allowed to reach a high level, salinity will also rise due to the build-up of sodium nitrate.

4

Disease Description and Treatments

The following section provides a summary of all the diseases listed on the Disease Diagnostic Charts, followed by some of the more successful treatments used by the author. There are always other treatments available, but the ones listed here have been found to be the most effective by the author. A book that is invaluable to the aquarist interested in trying other treatments is Nelson Herwig's *Handbook of Drugs and Chemicals Used in the Treatment Of Fish Diseases* (Charles C. Thomas Publishing, Springfield, Illinois.)

TREATMENT ONE
Lymphocystis

Lymphocystis is unique in appearance compared to any other fish disease. It will appear as white or gray nodules that look like small pieces of cauliflower growing on the fins, although it can also appear on the body. It is not fatal or highly contagious, although if this infection occurs around the mouth it will inhibit the fish's ability to eat and can result in starvation if left untreated. Lymphocystis will usually clear up by itself. If it is posing a problem, the nodules can be removed with a pair of sterile tweezers. When the lymphocystis is removed, an antibiotic should be administered to prevent a secondary infection, but again be aware of the possibility of disturbing the filter bed. The best approach is to dab Mercurochrome on the spot where the lymphocystis was removed and avoid treating the aquarium with an antibiotic if possible. There are many products on the market that claim to cure lymphocystis in a matter of weeks, but the author has not had success with any that have been tried. The best treatment in most cases is to let the fish heal itself, provided the condition is not causing a problem with its normal activities.

TREATMENT TWO
Saprolegnia

Saprolegnia is a member of the class of *Phycomycetes* and can be recognized microscopically by the long filamentous hypae that are non- septae and sometimes branching. External fungus is nearly always a secondary infection attacking an open wound or ulcer. The mycelium of the fungus invades the skin and eventually the organs of the fish. This condition may result in death. The infection will appear as cottony growths on the fins or on the body usually near the fins. Many times a cure can be effected by treating the original problem, i.e., a bacterial infection.

To use an old adage, an ounce of prevention is worth a pound of cure, because fungal infections are usually a problem only if the aquarium is dirty or water conditions are not properly maintained.

Below are several treatments for external fungus, but keep in mind that fungal infections are difficult to treat, and success will vary depending on the seriousness of the infection and the constitution of the fish. Again, it is best to try and treat the original problem first because this will usually clear up the fungal infection also.

• **Maracyn** (by Mardel Laboratories) — a gram positive antibiotic that is sometimes effective against fungal diseases. This is most commonly accom - plished by treating the original wound that allowed the fungus to grow.

• **Maroxy** (by Mardel Laboratories) — an antifungal solution that is also effective, but the author has found it to be very stressful in teleosts and has also noted some disturbance of the filter bed.

• **Methylene Blue** — used at 2 ppm daily, or .2 ppm once every five days combined with the copper sulfate level in the tank maintained at .15 ppm. This should be continued for three treatments.

NOTE: TURN ALL CARBON FILTRATION OFF DURING ANY TREATMENT BECAUSE ACTI-VATED CHARCOAL WILL REMOVE THE MEDI-CATION.

TREATMENT THREE
Cyanide Poisoning

Indications of cyanide poisoning before the death of the fish is difficult and definite signs are not known. All fish that have come from the Philippines should be treated for cyanide poisoning as a precautionary measure. Some possible indicators of cyanide poisoned fish are (a) abnormal behavior such as a lack of regard for its own well-being, or (b) bloody patches that may appear. These are similar to ulcers caused by internal bacterial infection, and are probably caused by the production of occult hemoglobin due to the extreme stress the fish has been under.

It has also been mentioned by some authors that cya-nide poisoned fish rarely, if ever, contract *Oodinium*. This is probably due to the fact that these organisms feed off the blood-filled tissues, and the cyanide in the blood kills them. The author has had many fish die without any symptoms at all, but upon autopsy and conducting a picrate paper test, it was discovered that cyanide was the culprit. If cyanide poisoning is suspected before the demise of the fish, the following treatment might be of some value. (Taken from an article by Nelson Herwig in Drum and Croker.) Methylene Blue should be administered to act as an oxygen donor until the fish can rid its system of the cyanide. The Methylene Blue can be absorbed through the skin as well as the gills and therefore works well as an oxygen donor. As mentioned above, all fish coming from the Philippines should be treated in this manner as preventative maintenance. Do not use any medications containing formalin while using Methylene Blue because a toxic reaction can occur. Methylene blue should be administered at the rate of two drops per gallon. Treatment should be repeated when the blue coloration disappears.

NOTE: TURN ALL CARBON FILTRATION OFF DURING TREATMENT BECAUSE ACTIVATED CHARCOAL WILL REMOVE THE MEDICATION.

TREATMENT FOUR
Intestinal Trematodes

Fish with intestinal trematodes may not show any real signs of illness at all, or they may exhibit such symptoms as complete loss of appetite, drawn abdomen, and poor or faded coloration. The first signs to look for would be lack of appetite or finicky eating habits and the keeping of the dorsal fin down as they sometimes do when *Oodinium* is in its early stages. If trematodes are suspected, the food should be treated with Piperazine at the rate of 25 mg/10 g of food. This treatment should be continued for a period of 10-15 days. If the fish is not eating, treatment is considerably more difficult; however, the tank can be treated with Piperazine at the rate of 25 mg/gal. If no improvement is seen, the fish should be rediagnosed for more serious problems.

TREATMENT FIVE
Tuberculosis

Fish Tuberculosis (TB) is caused by *Mycobacteria Marinum*, one of the few gram positive bacteria that are pathogenic to fish. The first symptoms usually noted are shallow and rapid breathing. This symptom might continue for weeks without any other symptoms surfacing, although this is sometimes accompanied by loss of appetite and occasionally listlessness. Later the fish will hide a majority of the time or may stay at the top of the tank breathing rapidly and shallow. During the later stage of the disease, the abdomen will appear sunken or drawn and popeye may develop. The popeye is caused by infection of the optic tract. Similar symptoms accompany Ichthyophonus, so popeye cannot be a distinguishing feature of TB.

Because TB is an internal infection, it is difficult to treat. The infected fish should be moved to a hospital tank if possible, but can be treated in the main tank if necessary. Turn off all carbon filtration and treat with Isoniazid* at 40 mg/gal. If treated in a hospital tank, the water should be changed every two to three days, but if the main tank is used, change 25% of the water every other day and bring the Isoniazid back to treatment level. If the fish are still eating, the food should be soaked in an antibiotic that is effective in the treatment of TB such as Streptomycin sulfate* at the rate of 10 mg/100 g of food. The medicated food should be fed to all the fish exposed to TB. The treatment should be continued for two weeks and the medicated food should be fed for another two weeks. Following the treatment period, watch closely for any recurring symptoms.

Fish naturally have good resistance to TB and other

bacterial infections, so if these do pose a problem, you should probably take a closer look at the maintenance of your aquarium and the overall environmental conditions that are offered to your fish. Poor environment and poor diet are the primary causes of most diseases and therefore should be the first things analyzed. New arrivals should be fed food that has been medicated with Rifampin* at the rate of 6 mg/100 g of food. This should be given once a week for one month as a precautionary measure.

*These can be obtained through your local veterinarian.

TREATMENT SIX
Bacterial Infections

Bacterial infections are caused by a variety of organisms and are transmitted by a variety of methods. The only way to determine the exact pathogenic organism that is the source of the infection is through complex bacteriological laboratory techniques that are unavailable to the average aquarist. Therefore, we will make some generalities as to the pathogens by observation of the fish's symptoms. This is however the best method upon which to depend without the assistance of a pathologist to examine each fish. If conditions are watched closely, an extremely accurate diagnosis can be made.

Bacteria are divided into two groups, Gram Positive and Gram Negative. Gram Positive bacterial infections are far less common than Gram Negative. *Mycobacterium Sp.* are the only Gram Positive bacteria that this author has dealt with in marine fish that are pathogenic. The Gram Negative bacteria are *Pseudomonas Sp., Aeromonas Sp., Vibrio Sp., Chondrococcus Columnaris,* and *Myxobacteria Sp.*

If the infection is known to be Gram Positive then a Gram Positive antibiotic can be added directly to the main tank without any fear of destroying the filter bed. However, if the infection is Gram Negative, the fish should be moved to a hospital tank to prevent the chance of destroying the beneficial bacteria in the main tank. The pathogenic bacteria, however, are enteric and present in large amounts in the main tank, so an ultraviolet light or ozone should be utilized in the main tank to make future infections less likely.

Internal bacterial infections are the hardest to treat and the most difficult to recognize in their early stages. The most common and the most pathogenic internal infections are caused by *Vibrio Sp.*

The first sign of infection is a swelling of the abdomen which is sometimes accompanied by a reddening around the anus and possibly a bloody discharge. It is in this early stage that the infection needs to be treated because of the fast reproduction of the bacteria. *Vibrio Sp.* can reproduce itself once every 10 minutes and therefore can overwhelm its victim within 24 hours.

The second sign is evidenced by red patches appearing on the body. It is in this stage that the infection is usually first noticed. Unfortunately, it is also difficult to treat at this point. There are several antibiotics available for treating bacterial infections, but again, be careful about using any antibiotics designed for fighting gram negative infections because of the damage that can be done to the filter bed.

Listed below are several antibiotics and proper dosages that have been used by the author successfully:

- **Kanamycin** (by Aquatronics) - available in Spectro gram, 15 mg/gal.
- **Gentamycin** - available through your veterinarian, 15 mg/gal.
- **Erythromycin** (by Mardel) - available in Maracyn, 20 mg/gal.
- **Minocycline** (by Mardel) - available in Maracyn Two, 1 mg/gal.
- **Furabase** (by Mardel) - 30 mg/gal.
- **Tetracycline** (by Mardel) - 25 mg/gal.

All of the above antibiotics should be administered every other day for five days. During the use of any antibiotics, the lights should be dimmed so as to extend the life of the antibiotic.

These antibiotics can also be obtained through a veterinarian and used at the suggested dosage, repeated every other day for five days. To obtain faster results if the fish are still eating, the food can be treated with any of the following antibiotics:

- **Kanamycin** - 10 mg/100 g food
- **Gentamycin** - 10 mg/100 g food
- **Erythromycin** - 12 mg/100 g food

The use of any of these antibiotics should be confined to a hospital tank because of the effect it will have on the biological filter. The author has had reasonable success with Chloramphenicol used as an intraperitoneal injection. A solution of 1 mg Chloramphenicol per 1 cc distilled water is given at the rate of 1 mg/100 g of fish weight. Chloramphenicol has not been effective when dissolved in the aquarium as it is pH dependent.

As mentioned before, the use of any of the antibiotics designed to fight gram negative bacteria has ill effects on the biological filter bed. The only beneficial bacteria that the author has noticed affected is the *Nitrobacters,* which is recognized by an increase in nitrites.

NOTE: TURN ALL CARBON FILTRATION OFF DURING TREATMENT BECAUSE ACTIVATED CHARCOAL WILL REMOVE THE MEDICATION.

TREATMENT SEVEN
Brooklynella

Brooklynella Hostilis is a ciliated marine parasite. Unlike *Oodinium* and *Crytocaryon*, *Brooklynella* is not affected by copper maintained at therapeutic levels. *Brooklynella* attacks both the gills and skin of the fish. Fish infected with *Brooklynella* are listless, have a lack of appetite, show signs of respiratory distress, and usually excrete excess amounts of slime. Clowns infected with this organism nearly always excrete such large amounts of slime that it will appear as strings trailing the fish as it swims. The damage caused by the *Brooklynella* parasite is very extensive and also makes the fish susceptible to other bacterial infections.

TREATMENT AND PREVENTION

Formalin is the most effective treatment in combination with 3-minute freshwater dips. The infected fish should first be given a 3-minute freshwater dip unless the infection is so far progressed that large ulcerations are present. If ulcerations are present, the freshwater dip should be avoided because of the possibility of the fish losing large amounts of body fluid and thereby worsening the condition.

FRESHWATER DIP

Fill a small pail or tank with freshwater and dechlorinate. The freshwater needs to be the same temperature and pH as the main tank. If the pH is lower than the main tank, it can be raised by the addition of baking soda or other chemicals designed to raise the pH. Once the temperature and pH are the same, catch the fish without chasing and upsetting it. If the fish is stressed while being caught, place the fish in a small container of tank water until the fish has calmed down. Then place the fish in the freshwater for 3-5 minutes and return to the tank. Fish will react differently to freshwater. Some will go into shock immediately while others can be left in the freshwater for 20 minutes or more. If the fish shows signs of shock, such as lying on the bottom and losing color, return the fish to the main tank immediately. A freshwater bath is always a good idea before adding any new arrivals to the main tank.

Following the freshwater dip, the main tank should be treated with a 37% formalin solution at the rate of 15 ppm. All carbon filtration should be turned off prior to treatment. This treatment should be repeated every other day for three weeks. Quick Cure° by Aquarium Products contains formalin and malachite green and is very effective against *Brooklynella*. However, the malachite green will stain the silicone used to seal the corners in all glass aquariums.

The author has found that sometimes it takes up to four months to eradicate *Brooklynella* from the system. At times it would be easier to sterilize the tank and start over. If it is necessary to sterilize the tank, a solution of three parts water to one part Clorox° should be used. Afterwards, everything should be rinsed thoroughly and extra dechlorinator should be used when refilling the aquarium.

TREATMENT EIGHT
Ichthyophonus

Ichthyophonus is an internal fungal infection that is widespread and seems to occur without any selectivity. Virtually all fish autopsied by the author have had some of the ichthyophonus culture in one organ or another. There are no outward signs until the disease is well advanced and has already begun to destroy the liver, spleen, kidneys, and brain. The fish may show any or all of the following symptoms depending on which organs are infected and the stage of the infection: loss of appetite, loss of balance, poor color, deterioration of fins, listlessness, and sometimes popeye. There is no known cure that works effectively, but many are presently being experimented with. The best cure is prevention by keeping the fishes' immune system in good working order through good nutrition and a healthy environment.

Ichthyophonus shares symptoms with many other diseases. These common symptoms include deteriorating fins, loss of appetite, and sometimes popeye. The only symptom that points directly to Ichthyophonus is the loss of balance. This loss of balance is caused by the fungus beginning to infect the brain and spinal column.

If Ichthyophonus is suspected, the infected fish should be isolated, given good water conditions and a good diet. Again, for the time being, prevention is the best cure. Avoid overcrowding and isolate any fish that show any of the symptoms.

TREATMENT NINE
Gill Flukes

The first sign of gill flukes is rapid breathing. This is usually not accompanied by any other symptom except frequent scratching of the operculum. If the fish stops eating or becomes listless, then *Oodinium, Cryptocaryon,* or bacterial infection should be suspected.

Benedenia Mellenia are parasites that attach to the gills and skin of the fish. They range in length from 1/16" to 1/2" and are opaque and flat. They reproduce slowly, so several weeks might pass before an infestation of epizootic proportions would become apparent.

TREATMENT AND PREVENTION

The best treatment is a freshwater dip. If it is necessary to treat the entire tank, then dylox would be the best treatment.

FRESHWATER DIP

Fill a small pail or tank with freshwater and dechlorinate. The freshwater needs to be the same temperature and pH as the main tank. If the pH is lower than the main tank, it can be raised by the addition of baking soda or other chemicals designed to raise the pH. Once the temperature and the pH are the same, catch the fish without chasing and upsetting it. If the fish is stressed while being caught, place the fish in a small container of tank water until it has calmed down. Then place the fish in the freshwater for 3-5 minutes and return to the tank. Fish will react differently to the freshwater. Some will go into shock immediately while others can be left in the freshwater for 20 minutes or more. If the fish shows signs of shock such as lying on the bottom and losing color, return the fish to the main tank immediately.

DYLOX TREATMENT

All filter feeding invertebrates, shrimp, and crabs should be removed and placed in another tank during treatment. The main tank should then be treated with Dylox at a concentration of .25 ppm active ingredient. In order to figure the number of cc's of solution that will be necessary to obtain the desired concentration, use the following formulas:

1) Number of gallons in the tank x 3785 = number of cc's in the tank, then;
2) Number of cc's in the tank ÷ 1,000,000 x .25 ppm

(desired concentration of active ingredient) = number of cc's of solution needed if the solution is 100% active ingredient. (Let's call this number A), then;
   3) Take the % active ingredient and divide this into the desired concentration, (in this case .25 ppm). (Let's call this number B), then;
   4) Multiply A and B and the resulting number is the number of cc's of solution required to obtain the desired concentration of active ingredient.

> NOTE: TURN ALL CARBON FILTRATION OFF DURING TREATMENT BECAUSE ACTIVATED CHARCOAL WILL REMOVE THE DYLOX.

TREATMENT TEN
Hypercapnia

Hypercapnia is an excess of carbon dioxide in the blood and is caused by a high concentration of carbon dioxide in the water and is totally independent of the oxygen content. The only treatment for this is to increase the water circulation so as to increase gas exchange at the water surface. The lid of the aquarium might be left up so as to aid in gas exchange. If only one fish is showing signs of distress, then it is likely that the problem is a bacterial infection and Treatment Six would apply.

TREATMENT ELEVEN
Uronema Marinum

Uronema Marinum is a ciliated protozoan parasite that produces lesions similar to bacterial infections. In the beginning the fish will appear nervous and scratch from time to time on the bottom or on coral decorations. The scales will appear lifted with white patches or pale areas visible. Later the fish will hide more, and the white patches will become large lesions and will possibly hemorrhage. These lesions will look similar to Hemorrhagic Septicemia, which are caused by bacterial infections. Before the fish dies, it will remain at the top of the tank gasping for air and the ulcers will cover large areas of the body.

TREATMENT AND PREVENTION

A freshwater dip is the best treatment in the early stages, but in the late stages it could worsen the condition by opening the wounds and causing the fish to lose large amounts of body fluids. Indications of the late stages of infection would be bloody lesions or open wounds. In the late stages, the best treatment would be to fill a small aquarium or bucket with water from the tank containing the infected fish. The water should then be treated with Methylene Blue at a concentration of 3 cc/10 liters and Nitrofurozone at a concentration of 1 cc/liter. The infected fish should then be placed in this water for a period of 20-25 minutes. The main tank should also be treated with Formalin and Malachite Green, sold commercially as Quick Cure by Aquarium Products.

FRESHWATER DIP

Fill a small pail or tank with freshwater and dechlorinate. The freshwater needs to be the same temperature and pH as the main tank. If the pH is lower than the main tank then it can be raised by the addition of baking soda or other chemicals designed to raise the pH. Once the temperature and the pH are the same, catch the fish without chasing and upsetting it. If the fish is stressed while being caught, place the fish in a small container of tank water until it has calmed down. Then place the fish in the freshwater for 3-5 minutes and return to the tank. Fish will react differently to the freshwater; some will go into shock immediately while others can be left in the freshwater for 20 minutes or more. If the fish shows signs of shock such as lying on the bottom and fading colors, return the fish to the main tank immediately. A freshwater dip is always a good idea before adding any new arrivals to the main tank.

TREATMENT TWELVE
Oodinium Ocellatum

O. Ocellatum has a three-part life cycle consisting of (a) the dinospore or infective stage; (b) the vegetative form or parasitic stage; and (c) the encysted stage or reproductive stage. We will look at each stage separately and go into some detail.

The dinospore is a highly motile Dinoflagellate. The dinospore seeks a host for nourishment and commonly attaches to the gill epithelium most likely because of the increased vulnerability of this area due to the greater water circulation during regular osmoregulatory operations and because of the tenderness of these membranes. Many books have stated that if the dinospore does not find a host within 24-48 hours, it will die; but this may not always be the case, as some have been noted to live for up to four weeks without a host (Kingsford, 1975). The dinospore is the stage in which the disease should be treated and is the only stage in which complete eradication can be achieved. When the spots are noted on the fish, this will be the parasitic stage or possibly the encysted stage and will not be vulnerable to most treatments. Therefore, the tank should be treated for at least three weeks in order to eradicate the free-swimming dinospores and all the new dinospores that will be hatching out from the cysts already in the gravel and on the fish.

The second stage, the parasitic stage, is formed when

the dinospore finds a host. Upon connecting with a host, the flagellum are lost and the organism attains a rounded shape. Rhizoids begin to emerge from a funnel shaped aperture at one end. The rhizoids are similar to roots and penetrate the host cells in order to obtain nutrition. They also provide a way of holding on, thus preventing the fish from being able to scratch them off. This is the stage that is most commonly noted on the fish.

In the parasitic stage, the organism damages the gill epithelium by causing hemorrhaging and adhesion of the gill filaments. It has been said to cause death by interference with respiration, but many fish autopsied have relatively few organisms in the gills, and the question of toxin production is raised (Kingsford, 1975).

The third stage, the encysted stage, is the last stage of the cycle and is formed when the organism has obtained enough nutrients to supply it for some time. The rhizoids are retracted, and the opening is sealed with a cellulose material. The cyst then falls to the bottom of the tank or in some cases stays on the fish. This is where many aquarists think that the problem has cured itself, but nothing could be farther from the truth. The parent cell ends by giving birth to 256 free-swimming dinospores, all looking for a host. The rate of development is highly dependent upon the temperature, which is optimal at 25-27 degrees Celsius. When the temperature decreases to about 10 degrees Celsius, no division takes place. It takes about three days for division to be completed, and the dinospores are released into the water to reinfect the fish.

IDENTIFICATION OF THE INFECTION

The first sign of the infection is nearly always respiratory distress due to infestation of the gill epithelium. Breathing is usually fast and shallow, and the fish will be seen scratching on the bottom or on decorations. The above symptoms will nearly always be seen before the appearance of white powder on the body. This is the last stage of infection and is generally noted as white spots covering the fins and body of the fish, similar in appearance to a fish that has been sprinkled with salt. It will have a white, tan, or gold appearance. At this final stage, treatment should not be delayed; sometimes it is already too late for treatment because of the damage to the gill epithelium.

TREATMENT AND PREVENTION

The first treatment should be a freshwater bath:

FRESHWATER BATH

Fill a small pail or tank with freshwater and dechlorinate. The freshwater needs to be the same temperature as the main tank and also the pH needs to be the same. If the pH is lower, then add Sodium Bicarbonate or other chemicals designed to raise the pH. Once the temperature and pH are the same, catch the fish without chasing and upsetting it. If the fish is stressed when being caught, then place in a small container of the tank water until the fish calms down, before placing in the bath. Then place the fish in the freshwater for 3 minutes and return to the tank. If the fish shows signs of shock, i.e., laying on the bottom and fading colors, return the fish to the tank at once. This is a good measure to take with new arrivals if they are to be placed in the main tank without being quarantined.

In freshwater, Oodinium absorbs water quickly and, therefore, expands and basically explodes. As a follow-up treatment, Copper Sulfate is usually the most effective, but there are other treatments available. If invertebrates are in the tank, most medications have to be avoided or the invertebrates will have to be moved to another tank during treatment. The author uses Dylox weekly to eradicate any parasites that might be introduced to the tanks, but this also is toxic to some invertebrates. Filter feeders, shrimps and crabs are the only ones that have been affected in the author's tanks. If Dylox is used, the dosage should be .25 ppm active ingredient. During any treatment all carbon filtration should be turned off since the carbon will remove the medication. Dylox is extremely toxic to sharks, rays, and octopus. Toxic reactions to this drug include respiratory distress, loss of appetite, and loss of balance. Dylox is not as effective on Oodinium or Cryptocaryon as Copper Sulfate or Quinacrine Hydrochloride but does work if used on a regular basis.

COPPER SULFATE TREATMENT

Remove all invertebrates to another tank. Before placing Inverts in the new tank, give each one a 2-minute freshwater bath:

FRESHWATER BATH

Fill a small pail or tank with freshwater and dechlorinate. The freshwater needs to be the same temperature as the main tank and also the pH needs to be the same. If the pH is lower, then add Sodium Bicarbonate or other chemicals designed to raise the pH. Once the temperature and pH are the same, catch the fish without chasing and upsetting it. If the fish is stressed when being caught then place in a small container of the tank water, until the fish calms down, before placing in the bath. Then place the fish in the freshwater for 3 minutes and return to the tank. If the fish shows signs of shock, i.e., laying on the bottom with fading colors, return the fish to the tank at once. This is a good measure to take with new arrivals if they are to be placed in the main tank without being quarantined.

Treat the main tank with a citrated Copper Sulfate solution bringing the copper level to .25 - .30 ppm. The coral substrate will absorb most of the original dose, and the level should be checked every 12 hours followed by the addition of more Copper Sulfate solution until the desired level is reached. Continue checking every 12 hours and redosing until the level remains constant. The copper level should be maintained at .25 - .30 ppm. for 10 days and then activated charcoal filtering can be restarted. After carbon filtration for 7 days, check the copper level. If the copper level is 0.0 ppm., the invertebrates can be returned to the tank after being given another freshwater bath for 2 minutes.

DYLOX TREATMENT

All filter feeding invertebrates, shrimp, and crabs should be removed and placed in another tank during treatment. The main tank should then be treated with Dylox at a concentration of .25 ppm active ingredient. In order to figure the number of cc's of solution that will be necessary to obtain the desired concentration, use the following formulas:

1) Number of gallons in the tank x 3785 = number of cc's in the tank, then;
2) Number of cc's in the tank ÷ 1,000,000 x .25 ppm (desired concentration of active ingredient) = number of cc's of solution needed if the solution is 100% active ingredient. (Let's call this number A), then;
3) Take the % active ingredient and divide this into the desired concentration, (in this case .25 ppm). (Let's call this number B), then;
4) Multiply A and B and the resulting number is the number of cc's of solution required to obtain the desired concentration of active ingredient.

> NOTE: TURN ALL CARBON FILTRATION OFF DURING TREATMENT BECAUSE ACTIVATED CHARCOAL WILL REMOVE THE DYLOX.

TREATMENT THIRTEEN
Cryptocaryon Irritans

C. Irritans also has a three-part life cycle consisting of (a) Ciliate or tomite, the infective stage; (b) Trophont or parasitic stage; and (c) Tomont or encysted stage. The first stage is the tomite which is a highly motile ciliated protozoan. The tomite must find a host within 48 hours or die. This is also the stage in which treatment is necessary in order to eradicate the organism. When the tomite finds a host, it develops a buccal cavity and a flexible feeding apparatus. The trophont is quite destructive, causing skin ulcerations and small white postules. They may also burrow under the skin, making treatment even more difficult. The trophont eventually stops feeding and encysts, thereby bursting out of the postule and falling to the bottom to reproduce. The final stage is the tomont which is non-motile. The tomont, unlike *O. Occelatum*, reproduces through unequal cellular division. After five to ten days several hundred new tomites are released to look for a host.

IDENTIFICATION OF THE INFECTION

The first sign of *C. Irritans* is usually several white spots on the body and fins. Unlike *O. Ocellatum* the gills are not generally infected first, so respiratory distress would not be an initial sign. The spots are small and resemble small pimples. The organism later begins to invade the gills and the blood stream. The fish's color will sometimes appear blotchy as the pigment cells are destroyed. *C. Irritans* can also cause corneal opacity which can result in blindness. Treatment is sometimes difficult because the organism imbeds itself under the epithelium where medication cannot reach it.

TREATMENT AND PREVENTION

As in *O. Ocellatum*, a freshwater bath is usually the best initial treatment. It does however, tend to be less effective than with *O. Ocellatum* because of the fact that *C. Irritans* embeds itself under the epithelium. This is the reason for sudden reappearances after treatment. Copper sulfate is a relatively good preventative medication but is not as effective on *C. Irritans* as it is on *O. Ocellatum*. Following a freshwater bath, the author has found that the best treatment is the addition of Quinacrine Hydrochloride to the aquarium at a rate of 10 mg/gal. This also seems to be safe for use with invertebrates other than filter feeders. To be sure any valuable inverts should be moved to another tank, such as anemones and live coral. Quinacrine Hydrochloride is available through a veterinarian.

FRESHWATER BATH

Fill a small pail or tank with freshwater and dechlorinate. The freshwater needs to be the same temperature as the main tank and also the pH needs to be the same. If the pH is lower, then add Sodium Bicarbonate or other chemicals designed to raise the pH. Once the temperature and pH are the same, catch the fish without chasing and upsetting it. If the fish is stressed when being caught, then place in a small container of the tank water until the fish calms down, before placing in the bath. Then place the fish in the freshwater for 3 minutes and return to the tank. If the fish shows signs of shock, i.e., laying on the bottom and fading colors, return the fish to the tank at once. This is a good measure to take with new arrivals if they are to be placed in the main tank without being quarantined.

QUINACRINE HYDROCHLORIDE TREATMENT

Anemones and live Coral should be removed to another tank after receiving a 2-minute freshwater bath. All carbon filtration should be turned off and the main tank treated with Quinacrine Hydrochloride at varying rates of concentration from 8-12 mg/gal. This dose can be made in two treatments of 4-6 mg/gal each treatment. Different manufacturers of Quinacrine Hydrochloride make varying concentrations so the label cannot be trusted. Obtain your Quinacrine Hydrochloride from someone who has already determined the correct dosage. You can also determine the correct dosage yourself by treating some inexpensive, healthy fish with different concentrations until the lethal dosage is determined. Half of the lethal dosage is then effective for treatment. The lights should be turned off since light slowly weakens the Quinacrine Hydrochloride. After 12 days the Quinacrine can be removed by carbon filtration and the inverts can be returned to the tank after 36 hours. The inverts should be given a 2-minute freshwater bath before being returned to the main tank.

5

Pathology and Laboratory Techniques

This chapter contains a brief introduction to the clinical and scientific determination of the causative organisms involved in disease and death of a fish. In order to understand the symptoms of diseases and the procedures for testing for disease, the foregoing chapters on diagnosis and treatment of fish diseases should be studied.

Following is a list of laboratory equipment needed to conduct a post-mortem examination:

- Microscope capable of 1000x magnification with color corrected lenses.
- Glass slides
- Glass cover slips
- Spatula
- Scalpel
- Tweezers
- Scissors
- Gram stains
- Ziehl Neelsen stain and decolorizer
- Dissecting tray

The first thing that should be noted is that a fresh specimen is of the utmost importance because soon after death many saprophytic bacteria begin to feed off the dead tissues, making it increasingly difficult to isolate the causative organism. The gills, liver, and kidneys begin to decompose after only a few hours, and other organs are also greatly affected within a short time after death. If the fish dies of unknown reasons, a systematic study would be in order. If the cause of death is known, then several of the following steps can be avoided. The following steps should always be followed in the case of an unknown cause of death:

1. External Examination

a) Red areas on the skin - *Oodinium, Cryptocaryon,* Hem–orrphagic Septicemia (caused by internal bacterial infections), pH or phenol burns.

b) Cottony wool lesions - *Saprolegnia*

c) Velvet-like turbidity - *Oodinium*

d) Raised scales - Internal bacterial infection, i.e., tuberculosis or *Vibrio Sp.*

e) Reddening of the anus - Intestinal bacteria, i.e., *Vibrio Sp.* or poor diet.

f) Popeye- Possibly accompanying internal bacterial infections such as tuberculosis but more often with fungal infections such as Icthyophonus.

g) Drawn or dull eyes - Starvation or water poisoning.

h) Frayed fins - Internal bacterial infection causing a marked circulation decrease or parasites.

2. Gills

a) Dark pigmentation - Circulatory obstruction possibly parasitic.

b) Swelling of the gill filaments - Irritation by parasites or poor water conditions such as contaminants.

c) Cottony growth - *Saprolegnia.*

d) Brown discoloration - Gill rot, Hypercapnia, cyanide poisoning, or nitrite poisoning.

e) Small yellow to clear worms - Monogenic trematodes.

3. Abdominal Cavity

a) Exudate, watery, or bloody -*Vibrio.*

b) Excessive fat deposits - Poor diet.

c) Worms in the abdominal cavity - various flat worms, round worms, or nematodes.

4. Digestive Tract

a) Inflammation of the alimentary canal - poisoning, poor diet, trematodes, or *Vibrio Sp.*

5. Liver

a) Yellow or pink discoloration - *Vibrio. Sp.*

b) Green discoloration - Biliary Stasis.

c) Brown spots - Cirrhosis of the liver, possibly*Vibrio Sp.* or Ichthyophonus if accompanied by granulomas.

d) White cysts - Ichthyophonus or Tuberculosis.

6. Spleen

a) White nodules - Ichthyophonus, *Vibrio Sp.*

7. Kidneys

a) Bloody inflamation - *Vibrio Sp.*

b) Soft white cysts - Tuberculosis.

c) Hard white cysts - Ichthyophonus.

8. Swim Bladder

a) Inflamed or filled with blood - *Vibrio Sp.*

9. Heart

a) Yellow or white nodules - Ichthyophonus or tuberculosis.

10. Blood

A blood sample can be obtained from the heart or through the last vertebra. If the sample is to be taken from the last vertebra, an incision should be made just in front of the last vertebra. The last vertebra should be cut off, and then a blood sample can be obtained from the open vein. Fresh blood should be used or a sample that has been prevented from clotting by the use of 5% Sodium Oxalate. A blood cell count is of limited value because the normal values for most marine fish are unknown. The presence of rod, cocci, or other bacteria would indicate a bacterial infection. Red corpuscles that have burst would indicate ammonia or the presence of another toxic chemical.

The coagulase factor is also important because of the fact that cyanide acts as an enzyme inhibitor and therefore slows coagulation.

11. Muscles

a) Pelechia - *Vibrio Sp.*

b) Red colored worms - Nematodes.

c) Small white nodules - Ichthyophonus.

12. Bones

a) Osteomalacia - Vitamin deficiency, poor diet.

b) Growths on the bone - Osteosis, tumors.

13. Brain

a) White nodules-Ichthyophonus.

When a suspect sample is taken, a smear should be made and the proper tests run in order to verify the problem. The chart on this page will be helpful in identifying bacterial infections, although there will be exceptions. If the problem is not bacterial, the verification can be made under a microscope. An explanation of each causative organism is described in the following pages.

BACTERIA IDENTIFICATION CHART

USING GRAM STAIN

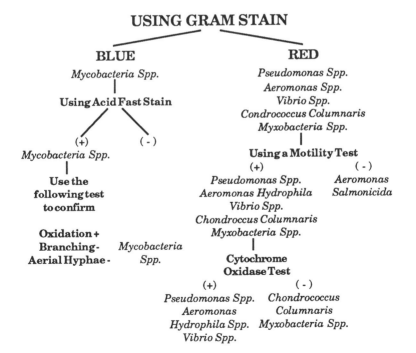

BLUE

Mycobacteria Spp.

Using Acid Fast Stain

(+)   (-)
Mycobacteria Spp.

Use the
following test
to confirm

Oxidation +
Branching -   *Mycobacteria*
Aerial Hyphae -   *Spp.*

RED

Pseudomonas Spp.
Aeromonas Spp.
Vibrio Spp.
Condrococcus Columnaris
Myxobacteria Spp.

Using a Motility Test

(+)   (-)
Pseudomonas Spp.   *Aeromonas*
Aeromonas Hydrophila   *Salmonicida*
Vibrio Spp.
Chondroccus Columnaris
Myxobacteria Spp.

**Cytochrome
Oxidase Test**

(+)   (-)
Pseudomonas Spp.   *Chondrococcus*
Aeromonas   *Columnaris*
Hydrophila Spp.   *Myxobacteria Spp.*
Vibrio Spp.

URONEMA MARINUM

Uronema Marinum is a ciliated protozoan parasite that can cause extensive damage to fish. The wounds often are confused with a bacterial infection. By examining a scraping from one of the lesions, many of the parasites can be seen. In a wet preparation at 100x magnification, they will appear quite agile and move very rapidly. The author has dealt with this parasite most often on Butterflies and Heniochus.

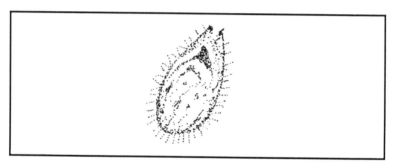

GILL FLUKES

Gill flukes can usually be seen on the gills as small black spots, but it is also possible that they will not be visible. If they are suspected, a slide should be made by cutting away several of the gill lamelae and making a wet preparation. At 200x, they will look like small cigars with various colored internal organs. Gill flukes is a broad term for a large number of various parasites. For this reason, not all will look alike, and it would be difficult to name all that may be encountered.

LYMPHOCYSTIS

The lesion is scraped off and onto a slide and is then squashed as thin as possible and the slide cover put into

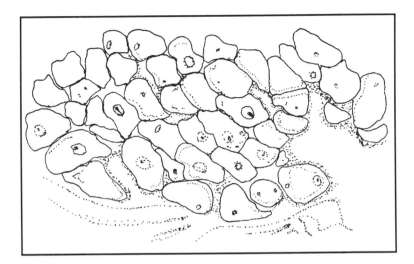

place. At 40x, large cells will be visible with flat sides touching each other. The cell walls will be thick and transparent.

SAPROLEGNIA

Saprolegnia is a member of the class of *Phycomycetes* and can be recognized microscopically by the long filamentous hypae that are non-septae and sometimes branching. This fungus is nearly always a secondary infection attacking an open wound or ulcer. The mycelium of the fungus invades the skin and eventually the organs of the fish and then causes death. These infections are usually caused by poor environment or poor diet which results in lowered resistance in the fish.

A slide should be prepared by taking a scraping of the infection and making a wet mount. This should then be stained by adding a drop of Gram stain. The mycelia will stain dark blue and will be non-septae and have occasional branching. If there is red staining occurring, this could indicate the presence of *myxobacteria* or possibly *saprolegnia*, if the specimen is dead, since many organisms that stain gram positive (blue) will stain gram negative (red) if dead or aging.

ICHTHYOPHONUS

If Ichthyophonus is suspected, a gill smear wet mount should be made and also a small section of the spleen or liver should be mounted on a slide. The spleen or liver should be air dried and stained with Brilliant Cresyl Blue. At 400x, irregularly shaped cells will be visible and round spores may also be seen.

TUBERCULOSIS

M. Marinum is a gram positive, acid and alcohol fast, non-motile, non-capsulate, and non-sporing bacteria. A scraping should be taken from the gills, liver, kidneys, and spleen. These should be air dried and fixed to the slide by passing the slide through the flame of a bunsen burner three times slowly. These should then be gram stained using the following method:

Flood the slide with methyl violet stain and allow it to act for 5 minutes. Wash the slide with iodine solution and allow the iodine to act for 2 minutes. Wash the slide with water and then rinse with decolorizer for 5 seconds followed by a rinse with water. Apply Basic Fuchsin for 30 seconds and rinse thoroughly with water. Allow to air dry and examine. If gram positive bacteria are seen that are slender rods and appear beaded, then another slide should be made and stained with acid fast stain using the following method:

Flood the slide with Ziehl-Neelsen Carbol Fuschin and allow it to act for 5 minutes, heating intermittently without making the stain boil or dry out. Add more stain as necessary to prevent drying out. Wash the slide with water and then flood with decolorizer and allow this to act for 1 minute and rinse with water. Do this several times. Apply Methylene Blue counterstain and allow it to act for 15 seconds. Wash with water and then allow to air dry.

> NOTE: TAP WATER MAY CONTAIN SAPRO-PHYTIC ACID FAST MYCOBACTERIA, SO THE WATER USED TO WASH THE SLIDE SHOULD BE KNOWN TO BE FREE OF THESE BACTERIA.

At 1000x, mycobacteria are noticeably red in contrast to the blue background and appear as straight or slightly curved rods about 3.0 μ microns x .3 μ microns with rounded or slightly expanded ends.

It is important to culture the bacteria in order to aid in identification by noting the type of colonies produced. The mycobacteria *M. Marinum* are strictly aerobic and grow well on Lowenstein-Jensen media kept at 37 degrees Celsius. Growth will appear after two to four weeks. The colonies will have a moist, smooth surface and will be buff to yellow in color.

INTESTINAL TREMATODES

In order to verify the presence of trematodes, a slide must be made from a scraping of the small intestines. This should be a wet mount. At 50x, the trematodes appear as large bodies that move in jerky motions. Numerous suctorial discs are usually visible.

CYANIDE POISONING

Cyanide poisoning is difficult to recognize before the demise of a fish and even then is not a simple process. Upon autopsy the first thing that will be noted is the fact that the blood does not seem to coagulate as rapidly as usual. The liver and the kidneys will show sign of necrosis along the edges and around major blood pathways. The only way to determine the presence of cyanide is the picrate paper test described below (from an article by Nelson Herwig in *Drum and Croker*).

"Picrate paper is prepared by soaking filter paper in a solution of 5 gm. of Sodium Carbonate and 0.5 gm. of picric acid dissolved in 100 ml. of distilled water. The solution keeps indefinitely, but the papers, after drying, retain their strength for only a few days, so prepare more or less as needed. To make the test, crush or macerate some of the suspected fish organs or stomach contents and place in a small amount of distilled water in a test tube. A few drops of chloroform will hasten autolysis. Suspend a piece of picrate paper, slightly moistened, by a cork at the top of the tube allowing for an air space between the mixture and the paper. Maintain the tube upright at a temperature of approximately 30° to 35° C. The appearance of a brick red color in the previously yellow picrate paper indicates the presence of hydrocyanic acid. A mild reaction, one appearing after one to several days, indicates what are probably non-toxic amounts of cyanogenic substance (chronic toxicity). A well-marked red coloring appearing after only a few hours is definitely significant (acute toxicity)."

Any new arrivals that had just started eating and died without apparent reason or with very little outward signs of necrosis should be tested for cyanide.

BACTERIAL INFECTIONS
(Gram Negative)

The bacteria that are of most concern here are the following: *Vibrio Anguillarium, Vibrio Parahaemolyticus, Pseudomonas Fluorescens, Aeromonas Liquefaciens,* and *Chondrococcus Columnaris.*

A scraping should be made of the lesion or infected

areas and the slide should be air dried and then stained with Gram stain using the following method:

Flood the slide with Methyl violet stain and allow to act for 5 minutes. Wash the slide with iodine solution and allow the iodine to act for 2 minutes. Wash the slide with water and then rinse with decolorizer for 5 seconds followed by a rinse with water. Apply Basic Fuchsin for 30 seconds and rinse thoroughly with water. Allow to air dry and examine.

The gram negative bacteria will stain red and the gram positive blue. If a gram negative bacteria is found in large numbers, a culture would need to be made and the bacteria isolated. More tests can then be performed in order to identify the bacteria accurately. The chart at the beginning of this section shows the various tests for determining the presence of bacteria and the results. You should have a good understanding of various bacteriological methods and Kochs postulates. Also, you should obtain a good text that deals specifically with the identification of bacteria. Below is a brief description of the bacteria that are normally encountered as they appear under the microscope.

Vibrio Sp. - Polar flagellated, curved rods, gram negative, non-capsulate and non-sporing, approximately 3.0 μ microns x .5 μ microns.

Pseudomonas Sp. - Polar flagellated, relatively straight rods, gram negative, non-sporing and non-capsulate.

Chondrococcus Sp. - long thin rods and gram negative

BROOKLYNELLA

Brooklynella hostilis is a ciliated protozoan parasite. If *Brooklynella* is suspected, a scraping should be made from any body lesions and also from the gills and then should be made as wet preparations. *Brooklynella* invades the gills first and then spreads to other parts of the body. At 400x, the pear-shaped parasite can be seen. They are highly motile, and inside the organism several micronu- clei can be seen, including a ventral adhesion organ that is used to attach itself to the host. This ventral adhesion organ is also a good anatomical reference to differentiate this and other parasites.

Treatment and cure for Brooklynella are very difficult after the appearance of body lesions. Copper at therapeu- tic levels has no effect on this organism whatsoever.

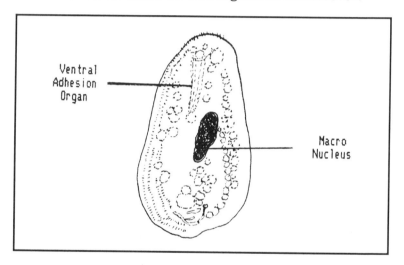

CRYPTOCARYON IRRITANS

A scraping should be made of the skin and the gills by scraping the skin directly onto the slide. This scraping should contain both mucus and scales of the infected fish. The gill scraping should be made in the same manner if the fish is moribund or dead. A drop of water should then be added to the slide and a cover slip put into place.

The first stage, the tomite, is a highly motile ciliated protozoan parasite that appears pear-shaped. At 100x, the cilia will be visible and the tomites are usually ex- tremely active as they seem to be always nibbling at debris. The buccal cavity begins to develop once the tomite finds a host. As the trophont or parasitic stage grows, the cilia shorten and the buccal cavity becomes smaller. The trophont eventually stops feeding and encysts to begin reproduction. The final stage, the tomont, is quite large and at 100x will appear very dark due to the many developing tomites. In five to ten days, the tomont will burst, releasing several hundred new tomites to find hosts.

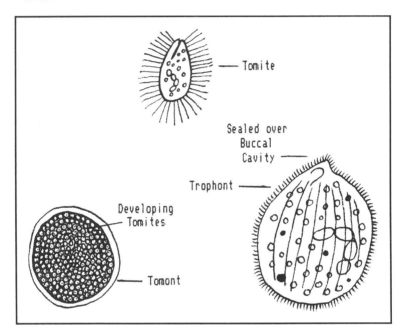

OODINIUM OCELLATUM

A scraping should be made from the skin and placed on a slide, and if the fish is dead or moribund, another slide should be made from the gills. These should both be wet mounts, which are made by placing the scraping on the slide, adding a drop of the tank water to the slide, and putting the cover slip in place. Again, it should be stressed that the fresher the specimen the better because many parasites will not be present or identifiable after only a few hours have passed.

Start with the lowest magnification when examining the slide and increase the power as you survey the specimen. In the case of *Oodinium*, the dinospore will appear as a small dot moving about irregularly at 150x. The vegetative form is visible at 40x but is not easily recognized. The vegetative or parasitic form will be much larger than the dinospore and is usually slightly egg-shaped and non-motile. At 400x, the rhizoids can be seen easily. The final stage or cyst looks very similar to the vegetative form except that the cytoplasm appears very dark and the opening where the rhizoids were is now sealed.

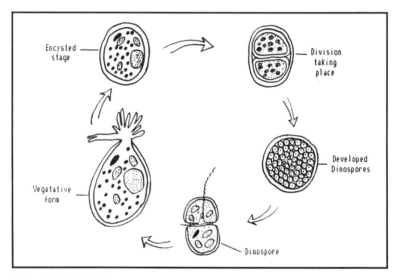

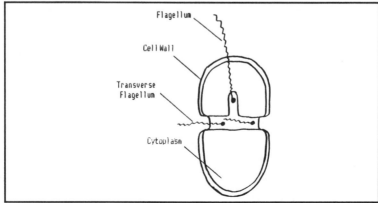

Appendix

References and Suggested Reading

1. Reichenbach-Klinke, H. *Fish Pathology.* Munich, Germany: TFH.

2. Bullock, G. *Bacterial Diseases of Fishes.* London, England: TFH.

3. Gillies, R. *Bacteriology Illustrated.* New York, N.Y.: Churchill Livingstone.

4. Macfaddin, J. (1980). *Biochemical Tests for Identification of Medical Bacteria.* Baltimore, M.D.: Williams & Wilkins.

5. Herwig, N. (1979). *Handbook of Drugs and Chemicals used in the Treatment of Fish Diseases.* Springfield, Ill. Charles C. Thomas.

6. Spotte, S. *Fish and Invertebrate Culture.* New York, N.Y.: John Wiley & Sons.

7. Spotte, S. *Seawater Aquariums, "The Captive Environment".* New York, N.Y.: John Wiley & Sons.

8. Kingsford, E. *Treatment of Exotic Marine Fish Diseases.* St. Petersburg, Fl.: Palmetto Publishing Co.

9. Moe, M. *The Marine Aquarium Handbook, "Beginner to Breeder".* Plantation, Fl.: Norns Publishing Co.

Glossary

Buccal Cavity - The mouth cavity of some parasites and nematodes.

Ciliated - Covered with minute hair-like cytoplasmic processes, which beat rhythmically to produce locomotion.

Ectothermic - A cold blooded animal.

Encysted - Enclosed within a cyst.

Epithelium - The top layer or layers of cells which line tubes, and forms the secretory portions and ducts of glands.

Epizootic - Attacking many different animals at the same time, used in reference only to diseases.

Flagellum - A slender, whip-like process of a cell as that possessed by certain bacteria, algae, protozoans, choanocytes and reproductive cells. It functions as a locomotor organ for propulsion of fluids and as a sensory organelle.

Hemoglobin - An iron containing respiratory pigment present in red blood cells of vertebrates and in the plasma of certain invertebrates.

Histolic - The ability to dissolve and breakdown cells in order to use them as nutrients.

Hyphae - A single filament of the mycelium of a fungus.

Intraperitoneal - Given in the visceral cavity to be absorbed by the intestinal walls or other organs.

Methemoglobin - Hemoglobin, oxidized and incapable of

releasing oxygen to cells.

Mycelium - A tangled mass of hyphal filaments which make up the vegetative body or thallus of a fungus.

Non-Septate - Not divided or not possessing septum.

Osmoregulatory - Pertaining to the regulation or control of osmotic pressure within an organism, accomplished by maintenance of proper water and electrolyte balance.

pH - Chemical designation used to express relative acidity and alkalinity of a solution.

Postule - A cyst or protective covering in which many parasites grow.

Rhizoids - A slender rootlike filament which attaches the mycelium of some fungi to the substrate.

Teleost - Any fish of the class Osteichthyes (Teleostomi), characterized by possession of a bony skeleton.

Viscera - The organs of the body, especially those of the abdomen.

Volume Conversions

Use the vertical column and follow the horizontal line across to the desired information. For example: How many drops are in one ounce? Find *ounce* in the vertical column and follow it to the right until you reach the column entitled *drops*. The answer is 600

	drop	tbsp	tsp	cup	gm	ft³	in³	ml	cc	oz	pt	qt	liter	gal
gal	76800	256	768	16	3785	.1339	231	3785	3785	128	8	4	3.785	—
liter	20275	67.6	203	4.23	1000	.0353	61.025	1000	1000	33.8	1.7598	1.057	—	.264
qt	19200	64	192	4	946.35	.0334	57.75	946.35	946.35	32	2	—	.95	.25
pt	9600	32	96	2	473	.0167	28.87	473	473	16	—	.5	.473	.125
oz	600	1.99	5.99	.1248	29.52	.001	1.8	29.52	29.52	—	.0624	.0312	.0295	.0078
cc	20.3	66.66×10^{-3}	.20	4.22×10^{-3}	1gm H_2O at 4°C	35.3×10^{-6}	.061	—	—	33.8×10^{-3}	2.11×10^{-3}	1.054×10^{-3}	.001	.0003
ml	20.3	66.66×10^{-3}	.20	4.22×10^{-3}	1gm H_2O at 4°C	35.3×10^{-6}	.061	—	—	33.8×10^{-3}	2.11×10^{-3}	1.054×10^{-3}	.001	.0003
in³	332.4	1.10	3.30	69.3×10^{-3}	16.39	5.8×10^{-3}	—	16.39	16.39	.576	.035	.017	.0164	.0043
ft³	574.5×10^{3}	1.915×10^{3}	5.745×10^{3}	119.6	28,316	—	1728	28,316	28,316	998.81	59.84	29.99	28.31	7.481
gm	20.3	76.8×10^{-3}	230.4×10^{-3}	4.8×10^{-3}	—	40.17×10^{-6}	69.3×10^{-3}	1ml H_2O at 4°C	1cc H_2O at 4°C	33.8×10^{-3}	2.11×10^{-3}	1.054×10^{-3}	.001 H_2O at 4°C	.0003 H_2O at 4°C
cup	4800	16	48	—	237	8.36×10^{-3}	14.43	237	237	8	.5	.25	.2364	.0625
tsp	100	.3333	—	20.83×10^{-3}	4.928	174.33×10^{-6}	.30	5	5	.1666	10.416×10^{-3}	5.208×10^{-3}	4.928×10^{-3}	1.302×10^{-3}
tbsp	300	—	3	.0624	14.76	522.21×10^{-6}	.9009	15	15	.4992	.0312	.0156	.0147	3.9×10^{-3}
drop	—	3.333×10^{-3}	9.999×10^{-3}	208.32×10^{-4}	49.28×10^{-3}	1.7433×10^{-6}	3.007×10^{-3}	49.28×10^{-3}	49.28×10^{-3}	1.666×10^{-3}	104.16×10^{-6}	52.08×10^{-6}	49.28×10^{-6}	13.02×10^{-6}

Useful Tables

Temperature Conversions

Centigrade (C) = (Fahrenheit -32) x 5/9

Fahrenheit (F) = (Centigrade x 9/5) + 32

English to Metric Conversions

Inches	x 25.4	= Millimeters
Millimeters	x 0.03937	= Inches
Grams	x 0.03527	= Ounces
Pounds	x 0.4536	= Kilograms

Index

About the Author

Robert R. Clifton has kept a wide variety of marine fish for more than 13 years. This book is based on his extensive, practical experience. At the present time, his research is being conducted on more than 2,000 gallons of marine fish and invertebrates. The author maintains that early detection and preventative maintenance are the most effective forms of treatment for aquatic diseases.